THERE'S A FLY IN MY SWILL

by Brant Parker and Johnny Hart

A FAWCETT GOLD MEDAL BOOK

Fawcett Publications, Inc., Greenwich, Conn.

In the WIZARD OF ID series:

THE WONDROUS WIZARD OF ID   D2571

THE KING IS A FINK   D2550

REMEMBER THE GOLDEN RULE   D2487

Only 50¢ Wherever Paperbacks Are Sold

If your bookdealer is sold out, send cover price plus 15¢ each for postage and handling to Mail Order Service, Fawcett Publications, Inc., Greenwich, Connecticut 06830. Please order by number and title. Orders accepted only for United States and Possessions. Catalog available upon request.

THERE'S A FLY IN MY SWILL

Copyright © 1967, 1968 by Publishers Newspaper Syndicate

Copyright © 1973 by Fawcett Publications, Inc.

Published by special arrangement with
Publishers-Hall Syndicate, Inc.

All rights reserved, including the right to reproduce this book or portions thereof.

Printed in the United States of America
April 1973

IS BLANCH SWIMMING TODAY?

NO... SHE'S OUT SHOPPING.

9-28

THERE'S A WHALE IN THE MOAT!

WHAT DO YOU CALL **THAT**?

THE BUSINESSMAN'S LUNCH.

Publishers-Hall Syndicate, 1967

10-19

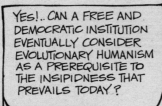

11-1

WHEN THE KING CALLS YOUR NAME, YOU WILL STEP FORWARD AND CURTSY...

11-10

...AND YOU WILL BE GRACIOUS AND DEMURE.

IT'S NOT **EVERY** WOMAN THAT GETS NAMED "MAN OF THE YEAR."

11-21

ALA KALOAM!

PooF

Paut Barker

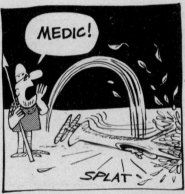

12-23

1-17

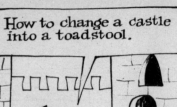

How to change a castle into a toadstool.

1-18

THAT'S ABSURD!

First, you say the words, "That's absurd"

Grant parker.

1-26 G. Parker

2-12

DING DONG

MAY I HELP YOU?

2-20

I'M LOOKING FOR SOMETHING **DIFFERENT** IN MEN'S SHIRTS.

ME TOO, HONEY.

G. Parker.

3-19